Spook Night!

CW00847830

Rachel Menzies

Illustrated by Emily Bornoff

Schofield & Sims

It is Spook Night in the town tonight.
It is the best night of the year!

Some children are scooping out pumpkins and turnips. They will be little lanterns on strings.

turnip

pumpkin

When it is d<u>ar</u>k, they dre<u>ss</u> up as a cat and an <u>ow</u>l. Can you spot the mi<u>ss</u>i<u>ng</u> t<u>ai</u>l?

cat <u>ear</u>s

<u>ow</u>l wi<u>ng</u>s

The <u>ch</u>ildren have some Sp<u>oo</u>k N<u>igh</u>t snacks. L<u>oo</u>k! <u>Th</u>is sandwi<u>ch</u> l<u>oo</u>ks like a monst<u>er</u>!

<u>sh</u>arp fa<u>ng</u>s

5

The children go out into the streets.
They see a bat! Can you spot it too?

bat wings

On Spook Night, <u>ch</u>ildren co<u>ll</u>ect sw<u>ee</u>ts in little bu<u>ck</u>ets.

Some <u>ch</u>ildren get hotdogs and some popc<u>or</u>n from a stand. They mun<u>ch</u> and crun<u>ch</u> <u>th</u>em.

Some <u>ch</u>ildren have some sw<u>ee</u>ts to t<u>oa</u>st. The sw<u>ee</u>ts t<u>ur</u>n to g<u>oo</u>. Yum!

Some of the streetlights go out.
It is so dark. The children jump
with fright.

There is no need to panic! The moon and stars are bright tonight and Mum has a torch.

It has b<u>ee</u>n a fun ni<u>ght</u>! What do you
<u>th</u>ink the <u>ch</u>i<u>ll</u> dre<u>ss</u> up as f<u>or</u>
Sp<u>oo</u>k Ni<u>ght</u> next y<u>ear</u>?